PETRIFIED FOREST

THE STORY BEHIND THE SCENERY

Petroglyphs near Newspaper Rock.

This book is dedicated to all who find Nature not an adversary to conquer and destroy, but a storehouse of infinite knowledge and experience linking man to all things past and present. They know conserving the natural environment is essential to our future well-being.

PETRIFIED FOREST
THE STORY BEHIND THE SCENERY®

by Sidney R. Ash and David D. May

Research Associate, Museum of Northern Arizona   Former Chief Park Naturalist, Petrified Forest National Park

Dr. Ash received his Bachelor's and Master's degrees at the University of New Mexico and earned his Doctorate from The University at Reading, England. Dr. Ash wrote the basic text of this book, and is the author of several publications on the geology of the Southwest.

Mr. May, a career employee with the National Park Service for over 10 years, served as editor of this book and added material in biology and environmental conservation. He studied a variety of natural history fields at the University of Illinois, and was graduated with major studies in zoology and ecology.

Book design by Robert Jacobson

Sixth Printing, 1981

PETRIFIED FOREST — THE STORY BEHIND THE SCENERY, PUBLISHED BY PETRIFIED FOREST MUSEUM ASSOCIATION, PETRIFIED FOREST NATIONAL PARK, HOLBROOK, ARIZONA 86025. L.C. NO. 70-91438. © 1969 PETRIFIED FOREST MUSEUM ASSOCIATION.

PETRIFIED FOREST is a land of quiet grandeur, a place of contrasts and change. It contains some of the largest petrified logs in the world, but you may best remember the exquisite color and pattern of a tiny chip of petrified wood. The park preserves the greatest concentration of petrified wood known to man, but a delicately balanced pedestal log may be more impressive than thousands of petrified logs scattered over acres of land. The endlessly varied hues of the Painted Desert (which makes up about half of the park) are a treat to road weary eyes, and the patterns of these intricately carved badlands are bewilderingly complex. The chances are that you will see no water in the park, but nearly all you see will have been produced by the action of water in geologically recent years. Short trails can take you from the sound of the road to the quiet of the hills. Ranger or naturalists will help you plan a longer hike into the Painted Desert Wilderness, where little has changed in thousands of years.

2

From a parking lot filled with modern cars, walk a thousand years into the past when ancient man made his home here. Just for fun, "read" the ancient petroglyphs that your predecessors here chipped into sandstone slabs. Deliberate a little on why there are only ruins here today, why man no longer builds pueblos here and why the Indians no longer farm the land. Give some thought to what this might mean to you, and to your descendants.

Petrified Forest offers to visitors an exercise in serendipity, the art of finding greater value in an activity than one would expect. What may start as a reluctant break in the high speed trip from one place to another, often develops into a totally new and different experience. To the visitor who takes the time to *enjoy* the park, rather than just "seeing" it, the few hours lost in the hectic rush to "see" another place are more than repaid.

The Forest That Was

Geologic time is divided into four units, called "eras." The first and oldest era was the Precambrian, followed in turn by the Paleozoic, the Mesozoic, and the present era, the Cenozoic. Each era lasted several hundred million years and is subdivided into "periods" which themselves lasted many million years.

Most of the rocks in Petrified Forest National Park are a part of the Chinle Formation, which was deposited during the last portion of the Triassic Period, early in the Mesozoic Era. The Chinle Formation contains many fossils, including the petrified wood for which the Park is most famous, and many banded and highly colored deposits which form the Painted Desert.

THE CHINLE FORMATION

The Chinle Formation is of Late Triassic age, about 200 million years old. It consists of a variety of rock types, most of which are soft, fine grained rock such as mudstone, siltstone, and claystone. The Chinle also contains some beds of much harder, more coarsely grained sandstone and conglomerate. Most beds do not extend over a great distance, but tend to become gradually thinner and disappear or to gradually blend into a rock of different texture.

In the Petrified Forest area, as in many areas of the southwestern United States, the Chinle exhibits a wide range of colors. Striking color variations, in fact, are the most noticeable characteristic of the Chinle Formation and usually make it easy to recognize. Many colors are the result of mineral compounds mixed into white or light colored deposits. Some deposits are composed of blue or gray clays. Various combinations of minerals, in beds of differently colored clays and sandstone, provide tones that seem to encompass all the shades of the rainbow. Iron oxides, in varying amounts, are responsible for the wide range of red tones in the Painted Desert.

The colors of the Painted Desert can change rapidly. What appears as a brilliant assortment of intense colors at one time may look dull and unimpressive at a different time. As a general rule, color is least intense at mid-day and is most brilliant very early and very late in the day. Following a rain, when the soil is wet, the colors are more intense than when the soil is dry and dusty. On a partly cloudy day, when the Painted Desert is a mosaic of light and shadow, the contrast between shaded and sunlit areas make the latter appear more brilliant.

The Chinle Formation, when exposed to forces of erosion for a short time, usually develops into badlands. The rugged badland topography results from the effects of climate on the alternating layers of fine grained, relatively soft material and coarser grained, more resistant rock. Sandstone, conglomerate, and lava flows resist erosion, forming cliffs and stimulating the development of mesas. Underlying beds of softer material erode much more rapidly, and tend to produce sloping hillsides and, when the protective layer is removed, often form conical mounds.

Most sediments that make up the Chinle Formation were deposited by streams meandering across a broad plain of fairly low relief in which is now eastern Arizona. The streams originated in the mountainous region called the Mogollon Highland that existed during the latter part of the Triassic Period in southeastern Arizona and New Mexico. In the vicinity of the Petrified Forest, the streams flowed north or northwest toward the sea, which was then just west of the modern Colorado River in southern California. Scattered across the plain were many lakes, large swampy areas, and some active volcanoes.

From the close of the Triassic Period through the end of the Mesozoic Era, deposition continued in the park area. The Chinle Formation was eventually buried beneath younger sediments approximately

3,000 feet thick. Some of the rocks covering the Chinle were deposited by streams and rivers while the area was above sea level, but additional sediments were deposited beneath a vast inland sea at a later time. As the sea retreated from western United States about 70 million years ago, deposition ceased for a time and erosion once again began to strip material from the land. The erosion cycle continued for many millions of years, into the Cenozoic Era, removing all of the rock overlying the Chinle Formation in this area. Erosion did not stop in this area until about 11 million years ago, when changes in southwestern drainage patterns set the stage for another major development.

BIDAHOCHI FORMATION

In the Tertiary Period of the Cenozoic Era, one of the principal rivers draining northeastern Arizona was blocked by uplift of land to the east. Waters from the ancestral Colorado River continued to flow in from the north, forming an extensive impoundment now called Lake Bidahochi (or Hopi Lake). Beneath the spreading waters of Lake Bidahochi, sand, silt, clay and other sediments flowing in with the ancestral Colorado River and other streams gradually accumulated. About 10 million years ago, the growing drainage pattern of the Hualapai Drainage intercepted the route of the ancestral Colorado River. As a result, water which had formerly flowed into Lake Bidahochi was diverted to the west and Lake Bidahochi was drained. Development of the ancient Hualapai drainage system and diversion of the ancestral Colorado River were crucial steps in the development of the Grand Canyon. Merrill D. Beal's excellent book on that great National Park (*Grand Canyon, The Story Behind the Scenery*) is specially recommended as a source of further information.

About 4 million years ago, volcanoes erupted in the vicinity of the drained bed of Lake Bidahochi, covering the lake sediments with layers of lava and volcanic ash. More sediments were deposited over the volcanic rocks by streams and rivers for a time but erosion once again became dominant in central Arizona. Streams and rivers eventually carried away all but a few remnants of the Bidahochi Formation from the park area. Light colored sandstone and mudstone on top of Pilot Rock, on Chinde Mesa, and at Chinde Point, as well as dark lava at Chinde Point and Pilot Rock, appear to be all that is left of the Bidahochi Formation at Petrified Forest National Park.

The cycle of erosion that stripped away the Bidahochi Formation also cut deeply into the Chinle beneath it, revealing large concentrations of petrified wood and other fossils. Some of the sediment removed by erosion in the last several thousand years has not travelled far, but has been redeposited in broad valleys, such as that of the Puerco River. Much of the eroded material, however, was swept into the Little Colorado River, through the Grand Canyon, and ultimately reached the Gulf of California. Today waters flow through much of the same route, but most of the eroded sediment now accumulates behind Hoover Dam, in Lake Mead.

The erosion cycle continues, and each year a little more petrified wood and other fossils are exposed to view after nearly 200 million years of burial. Recent studies suggest that about one quarter of an inch of soil is removed from the steeper slopes each year. Less than half of that amount is removed from gentle slopes and a still smaller amount in level areas. In localized areas, the vagaries of wind and water may cause deposition for a short time, but the present long time trend is toward removal of material.

SLASHING RAIN, *at times, beats upon the land. Water loosens and bears away unprotected soil, but areas beneath harder rock remain. In time, resistant sandstone and petrified wood "umbrellas" are perched upon pedestals formed of the protected soil.*

TRIASSIC LIFE OF THE PETRIFIED FOREST

Plant and animal life was abundant in this area during late Triassic times, but little of it would seem familiar to us today. A few plants and animals would have looked something like modern species, but the superficial similarities would have been overshadowed by the many differences. Some plants may have looked like giant copies of modern species.

In many ways, this area looked a bit like a mixture of jungle and marsh. Trees rose 200 feet above tangled undergrowth in places, and there apparently were wide expanses of marsh and swamp. The species of plants were very different, but this area may have looked then as parts of the Everglades look today.

Fossils found here indicate that clams, snails, fish, amphibians, and reptiles (perhaps including the first dinosaurs) were present in this area. We cannot now learn all the details of their lives among the great trees that have since been petrified or in the swamps and ponds of that distant time. Just as the tree fossils (petrified wood) and other plant fossils tell us much

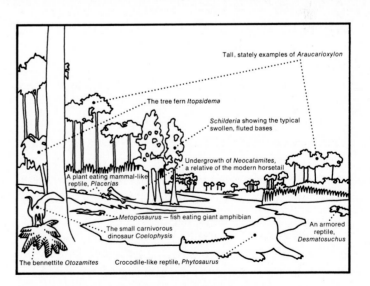

IN A LANDSCAPE *strange to today's arid Southwest, ancient plants and animals lived and died, leaving fossil remains from which we might deduce the appearance and some of their habits. Fishes and clams were also present, the latter in such great numbers that large deposits of tiny clam shells may today be found in the park.*

7

about the vegetation, however, fossilized animal remains tell us much about the living animal.

We can deduce from skeletons the dimensions and some habits of many early creatures. The size and shape of leg bones tell us much about how the animal moved about, whether it sprawled in the swamps or ran about on land. Preserved teeth are very informative, for they are the clue to any creature's diet. If the teeth were suited only for holding and tearing flesh the owner was a predator. Very different teeth are required to bite and chew vegetation. An intermediate type of tooth indicates the more varied diet of creatures who, like most of us, liked salad with their steak.

Our knowledge of Triassic life is the product of hours of labor by scientists. Their deductions are based not only on their work here, but on comparison to the other studies throughout the world.

We can today visualize and partly reconstruct the Triassic scene due to research but also due to a remarkable series of coincidences. Viewing the great quantities of petrified wood and the other fossils exposed at Pertified Forest may make it difficult to believe that plants and animals rarely are fossilized, but such is the case. Plants and animals normally decay and completely disappear relatively soon after death. When "just right" conditions prevail, some specimens or parts of them are preserved as fossils. Even after fossils form, they may later be destroyed by natural events or they may simply be deeply buried and remain unknown to man.

Here at Petrified Forest, however, conditions were such in the late Triassic that a very large number of tree trunks, some fern leaves, other plants, and some animal remains were preserved as fossils. Most of the leaves, reproductive structures, and other smaller parts were preserved as "compressions." Compressions are formed when most of the organic material is pressed out of plant parts by the immense weight of rock layers above them. Only the thin and extremely tough cuticle or "skin" of the plants is preserved. When the enclosing layers of rock are carefully removed, the compression fossil looks like a thin layer of carbon pressed against the rock. Many compressions show great detail, and are very valuable in helping research scientists reconstruct prehistoric plants.

Most of smaller fossils were preserved as compressions, but trees, bones, teeth, and other animal parts were petrified ("turned to stone") by a process that is not clearly understood. Most tissue (wood, flesh, bone, teeth, etc.) consists largely of numerous small spaces held together by rather little solid material. Various pores, tubes, and channels are hollow,

and even the individual cells are essentially microscopic cavities. In living tissue, the various spaces are filled with liquids. After death, softer tissues such as muscle tend to decay rapidly and so are seldom preserved by petrification. Harder tissues, such as bones and tree trunks, are much slower to decay. The rate of decay depends largely upon the environment in which an individual object is found. Temperature, moisture, oxygen supply, and other factors may have a profound effect. If oxygen is not available, for example, the microscopic organisms that cause decay are excluded and a log or bone may last for a very long time.

Northeastern Arizona, 200 million years ago, was a low lying, swampy area. Ponds, mud banks, marshes, sand bars, and swamps were traversed by streams and rivers that shifted and switched channels as wet and dry periods came and went. Many logs were apparently carried into this area by streams and rivers draining surrounding areas. Some logs became mired in mud or piled up in log-jams. Animals died, and their flesh decayed or was eaten by scavengers, leaving harder tissues. If nothing more

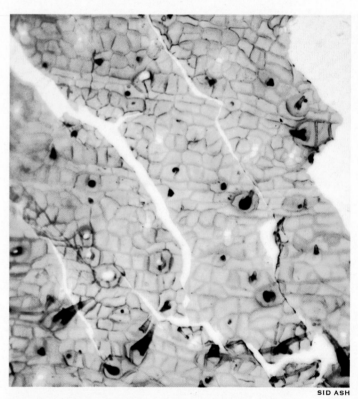

SID ASH

THIS PHOTOMICROGRAPH *reveals unaltered cuticle from one of the rare leaf fossils in the park.*

THE PETRIFICATION OF WOOD *may result in duplication of microscopic details of the wood or may simply fill the space occupied by the log without reproducing any detail. The photomicrograph at right shows both cellular replacement and less detailed filling of spaces with quartz.*

happened, the logs, bones, and teeth slowly deteriorated and returned their elements to the soil.

In thousands of cases, however, something did happen. The same streams that transported the logs also carried sediments from ancient mountain ranges. As rivers deposited their loads of sediment, and as the shifting streams moved sand and mud from place to place uncounted thousands of logs, bones, and other pieces of plants and animals were buried. As deposition of sediment continued, as the Chinle Formation grew thicker, more plant and animal parts were entombed in the growing deposit.

The swampy soils were saturated with water, and the water excluded most oxygen, thereby decreasing the rate of decay. The same water that slowed the decay of the logs had earlier filtered through sediments rich in the element silica. As the silica rich water slowly percolated through the logs and bones, the silica came out of solution and formed minute crystals of the mineral quartz within the spaces in the tissues.

In many cases, the growing quartz crystals filled the cell and other spaces without other changes occuring. In such cases, the petrified wood that resulted duplicates the original microscopic structure of the wood in nearly perfect detail. In many other instances, the cell walls were dissolved, and the growing crystals replaced the entire log without preserving any detail. Many logs display both types of preservation.

Most of the petrified logs here are completely petrified. All the tissue was filled or the entire space occupied by the log has been converted to silicon dioxide. Samples of petrified wood from some other areas seem incomplete, as if the petrification process had been stopped before the entire log was changed. Inside hollow logs, or in cracks in otherwise solid logs, the quartz crystals were not restricted in size by cell structure or adjoining crystals. Thus, in large spaces within the wood the crystals continued to grow. Large cavities within the wood are therefore sometimes lined with large crystals of amethyst, rose quartz, smoky quartz, and other gemstones.

Before the park was established and the wood protected, rock collectors often dynamited large logs in a search for the valuable crystals they sometimes contained. It was thoughtless and selfish activity of this type that helped arouse public support for establishment of the park.

The water that provided silica for petrification of wood, bones, teeth, and skin also contained other minerals which were added to the petrifying wood. Iron, probably the mineral most commonly incorporated into the petrification process, produced various reds, yellows, browns, and blues. Copper, included rarely, provided a lovely blue or blue-green. Manganese and carbon add black, and other elements produce a wide range of colors.

Look closely at pieces of petrified wood. Most, you will probably find, contain a wide range of tones that actually consist of blends of only three or four colors. Blends of yellow and red from iron, black from manganese or carbon, and the white or gray of the quartz can provide an amazing range of color tones.

Petrified wood and bone are surprisingly heavy. Quartz is very dense, and a petrified object is several times heavier that in its original form. A cubic foot of petrified wood weighs about 168 pounds.

PLANTS

Plant fossils are common in the Chinle Formation, the most abundant and obvious being the petrified wood for which the formation is well known. Less obvious and not so abundant are the remains of small stems, leaves, and reproductive structures, such as seeds and cones. At present about forty dif-

9

The leaf of the fern Clathropteris walkeri.
Slightly under natural size.

The leaf of the fern Phlebopteris smithii.
About natural size.

*Sketch of the trunk and leaves of a Bennettite
or "fossil cycad." One eighth natural size.*

IDENTIFICATION OF PLANT FOSSILS *usually requires
the examination of many pieces of fossilized
material. Geologists can sometimes find enough
pieces to reconstruct the plant, almost like
putting a puzzle together. Often, however,
there is no way of relating the many pieces until
discovery of an entire fossil solves the puzzle.*

ferent plant species are known from the Chinle Formation. Only about one quarter of them are based on petrified wood, the remainder being based on leaves, seeds, and other plant parts. Many of the prehistoric species were originally described from material collected in the park and have since been found at other localities in the Southwest. Plants that flourished here in Triassic times are now extinct, but some of their modern descendents now live in scattered parts of the world.

One of the more abundant groups of fossil plants known from the Petrified Forest is the ferns. Leaves of a large number of ferns have been collected, some so complete and well preserved that it is possible to study details of their epidermis through a microscope. Some fossil ferns compare closely to, and are probably related to, ferns now living in the humid tropical regions of the world.

The petrified stem of a rather unusual fern, *Itopsidema vancleavei* has been found in the area near Agate Bridge. Whereas most ferns have very short stems hidden in the bases of the leaves, *Itopsidema* had a thick upright stem and was more than three feet tall. The lower part of the stem is thought to have been soft, spongy, and sheathed in a mass of small roots. These roots apparently more or less buttressed the stem, enabling it to stand in an upright position. The stem was covered by the bases of old leaves and at the top was crowned by a tuft of living leaves. Superficially, *Itopsidema* may have looked like a miniature palm, but it was probably a distant relative of today's tropical "tree ferns" and was not a palm.

The fossilized remains of several kinds of seed plants, such as a now extinct group called the bennettites, are common in the park. Some bennettites had stout stems less than a foot tall topped by a tuft of large, coarse leaves, somewhat like a large fat pineapple with a cluster of leaves on top. Other bennettites had much taller, branching stems. One species, *Otozamites powelli*, bore leaves consisting of a heavy central stem with a row of stiff, oblong leaflets on each side.

Many of the trees which have been fossilized were large, some over 200 feet tall and 10 feet in diameter at the base. Most petrified logs are battered and worn, with limbs, roots, and bark broken or worn off. Relatively few stumps have been found in the position of growth with roots extending into the ground. The evidence indicates that most of the logs were transported some distance by streams before burial and fossilization here. While they were being moved, the limbs and roots were broken off, the bark removed, and they were abraded and battered.

Most of the petrified logs in the park are from coniferous trees. The great majority of the trees belong to a group named *Araucarioxylon*, distant relatives of the Araucarias now living naturally only in parts of South America, Australia, and New Zealand. Modern members of this family include the "Monkey Puzzle Tree" and Norfolk Island pine, both of which are used today in decorative planting. Fossilized twigs from several species of conifers have been collected here, and they, too, are thought to be relatives of the Araucarias. All of the twigs which have been recovered thus far are small and incomplete. It is thought that the twigs, like the tree trunks were transported some distance by streams from where they grew to the area in which petrification took place. Otherwise, larger, more complete and abundant specimens probably would be found.

The *Araucarioxylon* account for about 90% of the petrified wood found in the park. Two other varieties, *Woodworthia* and *Schilderia*, occur in scattered locations. Both tend to be much more somberly colored than the *Araucarioxylon*.

BURIED IN FINE MUD *about 200 million years ago, these delicate fern leaves were subjected to immense pressure when over 3000 feet of sediments were later deposited above them. Erosion gradually removed the overlying layers, exposing the fragile fossils to view.*

K. C. DEN DOOVEN

ANIMALS

No insect fossils have been found here, but indirect evidence suggests that insects of several kinds were present during the Triassic Period. Fossil insects have been collected from Triassic rocks in nearby areas, making it likely that insects were also present.

Teeth, scales, bones and other remains of several types of extinct fresh water fish have been found in the Chinle Formation. *Semionotus* and *Lepidotus* were fish with heavily armored scales, and teeth which indicate that they were plant eaters. *Ceratodus* is closely related to modern lungfish which live in small streams and ponds in arid parts of Australia, South Africa, and South America. When the pool they live in dries up completely, lungfish may survive by burrowing into the muddy sediments on the bottom of the pool and staying in the damp material until the pond is filled with water once again. The presence of lungfish in the Chinle suggest that there were alternating wet and dry seasons in the southwestern North America during Late Triassic time, although this theory cannot be considered a proven fact.

Of the several four legged animals present here in the Late Triassic, some would have appeared vaguely familiar to us. Only amphibian and reptile fossils have been found in the park so far, but it seems quite possible that the remains of early mammals will someday be discovered. Some of the Triassic creatures resembled modern alligators and salamanders, but many others would appear very strange to us.

Eupelor, looking somewhat like a large salamander, was one of the Labyrinthodontia, a group that earlier had been a large and dominant family. Most of the labyrinthodonts failed to continue adapting, and *Eupelor* was one of the last of them.

Short, weak legs and a large heavy body suggest that *Eupelor* could not support itself on dry land, and that it sprawled in water and mud. Restricted to rivers, lakes, and swamps where it probably fed on fish and other small animals, it was well adapted to the wet habitat and was apparently very common. Large concentrations of *Eupelor* fossils are occasionally found. Unable to survive on dry land, many individuals presumably gathered in water holes during dry periods. As the water holes dried up, the animals died.

Several types of reptile fossils occur in the Chinle Formation, but the most abundant are the phytosaurs. They were large crocodile-like animals and were the dominant reptiles during most of late Triassic time.

11

The front of the skull and lower jaw of phytosaurs found here formed a long, narrow snout. The jaws were set with numerous sharp, conical teeth suggesting that it preyed upon fish and animals living near water. The body and tail were protected by heavy bony plates, fossilized pieces of which are very commonly found in the park. The nostrils were located on a dome shaped elevation between and in front of the eyes. This adaptation would have permitted the phytosaurs to remain submerged for long periods while seeking prey. Capable of moving about on dry land on their short, stubby legs and able to stalk prey while submerged, phytosaurs must have been efficient predators. Capable of moving from a pool as it dried up or of existing on dry land, they were better adapted to their changing habitat than *Eupelor* and thus survived longer.

Some other reptiles, such as the pseudosuchians *Typothorax* and *Desmatosuchus*, were also covered with heavy, bony plates, and must have looked somewhat like "armored crocodiles." The "armor plating," plus large, sharp spines on their sides must have served to help protect them from predators.

Many people today think of all prehistoric reptiles as dinosaurs, but the term "dinosaur" actually refers to a particular group of prehistoric reptiles. The earliest known dinosaur in this region was *Coelophysis*. Compared to the better known giants that evolved later, *Coelophysis* seems almost puny. It was about 8 feet long and weighed only about 50 pounds. At a much later time, the gigantic sauropod dinosaurs reach a length of 80 feet and a weight of 50 tons. Nothing larger has ever lived on land, and our 50 pound *Coelophysis* would seem insignificant in comparison. *Coelophysis* fossils have not yet been found in the park, but do occur in other parts of the Chinle Formation in the Southwest. It is reasonable to assume that they did occur here and that fossil proof will someday be discovered.

Triassic animals differed from today's as much as or more than did the plants. Triassic animals evolved characteristics that suited conditions of the time, just as all living things on earth today have developed adaptations to present conditions. Amphibians had been the dominant animals during the latter part of Paleozoic Era. Toward the close of that era some amphibians proved unable to adapt to changing conditions and thus declined, many forms becoming extinct. Reptiles proved better able to adapt to the changes, evolved many new forms and were still on the increase during the Late Triassic. The first small dinosaurs appeared at the time of our story, and later developed many variations, but the dinosaurs, too, eventually disappeared.

The first small mammals evolved about the time of our story. When the reptiles were unable to adapt to changing conditions and declined, the mammals were able to keep pace with the changes. In time, man appeared and for the first time there was a form of life with the power to greatly alter and partly control the environment. The power to control was accompanied by intelligence enough to foresee the effects of changes. The ascendancy of man resulted in world wide changes, and creatures unable to adapt to those changes declined. Many sank into extinction, and others are following them now. A few have been snatched from the verge of extinction to survive a few more decades (after eons of evolution). Continuing and accelerating man-made changes in the environment, however, offer the threat of extinction not only to other animals, but to man himself.

SUGGESTED READING

BREED, WILLIAM J., *The Age of Dinosaurs in Northern Arizona*, Museum of Northern Arizona, Flagstaff, Arizona. 1968.

BREED, WILLIAM J., and Others, *Symposium on the Chinle Formation*, Museum of Northern Arizona, Flagstaff, Arizona. 1969.

DAUGHERTY, LYMAN H., *The Upper Triassic Flora of Arizona*, Carnegie Inst., Washington, D.C. Pub. 526. 1941.

McALESTER, A. L., *The History of Life*, Prentice-Hall, Englewood Cliffs, New Jersey. 1968.

EXPLORING THE SOUTHWEST *in 1853, an army expedition followed this valley. Lt. Amiel Whipple reported finding great concentrations of petrified wood and named the stream bed "Lithodendron (i.e. stone tree) Wash." The three mile trip across the valley to the Black Forest provides today's hikers with much to admire in nature's colors and patterns.*

Man in Petrified Forest

Man has known Petrified Forest for over 1500 years, and early man apparently was well adapted to conditions here. More than 300 Indian ruins are located in the park. Not all of these were occupied at the same time, and they range in size from one room shelters to the 150 room pueblo on the Puerco River. No men lived here when the Spanish first explored the Southwest in 1540, and few have lived here since.

We do not know if any of the Indians in the Southwest recognized that some of the stone they fashioned into artifacts had originally been wood. John Wesley Powell, one of the early explorers of the Southwest, did say that the Paiutes of southern Utah believed the petrified logs to be the arrow shafts of their thunder god, Shinuav. Perhaps they had observed the similarity of the logs and growing trees. Navajo Indians who lived to the north of the Petrified Forest region for several hundred years believed the logs to be the bones of Yietso, the "Great Giant" or monster that their forefathers killed when they arrived here.

Archaeologists have excavated several ancient villages at Petrified Forest. Just as fossils of ancient ages allow scientists to infer much about prehistoric plants and animals, the remains of early Indian residence tell us much of life here in the last 1500 years. Certain types of pottery, tools, and other artifacts help establish the period of occupation. Methods and materials utilized in constructing houses and storage rooms also tell us much. Architectural styles, color and form of pottery, and development of other artifacts are often typical of a specific time and place. Styles change, or evolve, and ideas spread from place to place. The patterns of change and movement can sometimes be understood by meticulous study of ruins, and their contents, and can tell us a great deal about the prehistoric Indians of Petrified Forest.

The early residents of what is now Petrified Forest National Park lived in close harmony with their surroundings. Most pottery, tools, houses, and clothing were fashioned from local materials. Coral, turquoise, shell, and other materials not naturally occurring here or nearby are found in ruins, and such items were apparently obtained from other Indians through trading. Foods were limited to plants that could be grown in this climate and animals that lived here and could be captured. Man was a part of his environment then even as we are now, but he was a closer part, more immediately influenced by environmental fluctuations. A dry year meant poor crops and little food the next winter. Man's con-

tinued existence depended upon there being no drastic environmental changes of long duration. It is equally true today; man cannot survive long lasting deterioration of his habitat.

During the 13th century, southwestern North America lay in the grip of recurring droughts. Vegetation decreased and animal populations dwindled. Farming in many places became impossible, and the human population in those places could no longer continue. As man could no more adapt to the drought than could the plants and wildlife, he either moved to a water supply or died. The great cliff dwellings and hundreds of other communities in the Southwest were deserted and have never been reoccupied.

In the Petrified Forest area, the extended period of drought brought one way of life to an end and stimulated the development of new fashions. As their environment changed, the Indians adapted to the changes by developing new farming methods, new styles of construction, and other new customs. The recurring droughts constituted a major environ-

mental change which men could not control, but successful adaptation to the change made it possible for them to survive. Still later, additional environmental changes developed to which the Indian could not adapt, and in the early 1400's the pueblo inhabitants were forced to either move or die.

Whether the displaced Indians would ever have returned to their old ways is unanswerable, for further changes began in the 1500's. Early Spanish explorers were followed by missionaries and explorers from the south. They were soon joined by other "new Americans" flowing in from the east and competition for land, water, and space grew apace. The occupation of their lands by men with a more advanced technology was still another change to which the Indians could not immediately adapt, although in time they were to begin a very successful adaptation to their new neighbors.

FLATTOP VILLAGE

The oldest ruins in the park to have been studied in detail are those of a village on the Flattops, iso-

MAN CAME *and made his home here. He built his walls of petrified wood, and from the wood made ornaments and his tools. He farmed the valley soils and asked his gods to provide the needed rain. His life was so closely linked with his environment that even minor changes could destroy his culture. We may never know why man left Agate House, nor where he went, but we believe that changing weather patterns evicted him. Today, we also live in a changing, deteriorating environment that threatens to destroy our culture, but we cannot move to a better place.*

K. C. DEN DOOVEN

Following page by David Muench.

lated mesas in the southern portion of the park. This site, partly excavated by Dr. Fred Wendorf during 1949, may have been occupied as early as A.D. 300 and was abandoned by the year 600. The village consisted of twenty-five round to oval pit houses scattered about the mesa top. Those excavated have long, narrow, eastward-facing entryways and most houses were 9-12 feet in diameter. They had been dug one to two feet into the underlying rock material and the underground portion was lined with thin slabs of sandstone set on edge. It is probable that the walls and roof were made of brush.

Many artifacts were found at the Flattops site. Those of stone include grinding stones, hammerstones, pipes, blades, scrapers, and numerous projectile points. About 60% of the stone artifacts are made of other locally available materials such as sandstone and chert. Many fragments of pottery also were found, and reconstructed vessels include bowls, jars of several sizes, ladles and one vessel in the shape of a duck. Most of the pottery used by these Indians is gray or tan to light red in color and is undecorated.

Twin Butte Village

Excavations at the somewhat newer Twin Butte Village demonstrate that cultural changes were taking place, such as increased organization of the village itself. Twin Butte Village consists of at least fifteen separate units scattered over an area about one-half mile square. Each unit is composed of one or more pit houses with several semi-subterranean storage structures, the latter usually arranged in a crescent behind the pit houses. Several apparently isolated, semi-underground storage chambers also are scattered about within the village. Pit houses were dug three to four feet into the ground and posts supported the roof, which may have been constructed of brush and logs. Entry to the Twin Butte houses was gained via a hole in the roof. Of the houses studied in some detail, one had mud plastered walls and another relied only on sandstone slabs more like houses at the Flattops. Other innovations included small storage pits in the floor and a ventilating shaft at one side.

Other cultural changes are reflected in styles of pottery, jewelry, and various implements. Stone tools had become more varied and arrow or spear points had changed styles. Much of the pottery found at Twin Butte is a gray ware similar to that from the older Flattop site, but new ideas were making inroads in old customs, and some of the Twin Butte gray pottery is decorated. The Flattop site pottery was all plain, but a few Twin Butte pieces show geometric designs or figures on the gray or white

DRIVEN FROM OTHER HOMES by their changing environment, the ancient people built large villages near dependable water supplies in an attempt to escape the drouth. Here, on a hill above the Puerco River, 250 people made their home. Driven on again, by further changes in weather patterns, the people vanished from this land. Crumbling walls, and POTSHERDS SCATTERED amidst the remnants of the ancient forest, are mute testimony to man's conflict with his world. Pottery that once served as cooking or storage vessels, that once was a part of men's lives, today serves only to excite later man's imagination.

background. About half of the pottery found at Twin Butte Village is a plain brown ware such as was being made by the Mogollon people to the south and east. It was probably obtained by the Twin Butte people by trade, perhaps in exchange for articles made from petrified wood. Artifacts made from shells and bone including awls, needles, pendants, beads, and bracelets were also found at the Twin Butte site. The shells are of marine origin and probably came, via trade with southern and western tribes, from the Gulf of California and Pacific Ocean.

Eight human burials were found during Wendorf's excavations at Twin Butte. All were very poorly preserved and consisted of few bones. It was apparent that most had been buried in the same position and had been accompanied by grave offerings, indicating the development of death ceremonial practices. The dead had been placed in their graves lying on their backs, with the head oriented to the west or southwest and the knees flexed. Pottery

PHOTOGRAPHS BY MIKE MCKELVEY

bowls, clothing or blankets, food, awls, beads, pendants, and bracelets were among the items found in conjunction with the burials.

It is not known whether the older Flattops Village was a permanent place of residence or summer community. There is some evidence (but no proof) that it may have been occupied each summer while the adjacent lands were farmed, but that an unknown alternate site was people's winter home. The greater organization of the Twin Butte village, the large food structures, and other factors make it apparent that the Twin Butte site was occupied all year.

Adjacent to the village are low stone structures which may have been part of stone and brush windbreaks in patches of farmed land. Very similar windbreaks are used today by Hopi Indian farmers to reduce wind blown sand movement. They probably also reduce moisture loss. If the structures at Twin Butte were in fact related to farming, it indicates that summer rainfall was adequate to support crops.

There is no evidence of any other source of water for crops, such as irrigation canals, and some of the farm lands are located on hillsides where water retention would not have been great.

The Twin Butte villagers, like all prehistoric peoples, lived in close harmony with their environment. They existed within limits imposed by environmental factors over which they had no control, such as rainfall. Even fairly minor changes in weather or other environmental factors could cause changes in the time of year when rain is received, for example, and could convert a formerly thriving area to one that was unhabitable.

PUERCO INDIAN RUIN

A series of droughts, beginning in A.D. 1215 and continuing until 1299, wrought major changes in Indian culture of the Southwest. What had been a dispersed population in small villages, groups of few family units, and other isolated developments could

THE STRUGGLE FOR EXISTENCE *was unending, and his life could not have been easy, but man still found the means of expressing his spirit. On weathered sandstone blocks, our predecessors here inscribed designs and figures. Their entire meaning is now obscure, but some petroglyphs are identical to clan symbols used today by modern Indians. Others may be religious symbols or simple doodling, and a few are plainly "dirty pictures." The original meanings, if any, are now lost, but ancient man's artistic endeavors endure until the rocks crumble.*

no longer persist. As weather patterns changed, adaptation to the changing environment became necessary to survival. The old ways of life were no longer adequate, and new customs evolved.

Although summer rains were no longer adequate to support farming everywhere on the plains, some areas remained livable. Along major drainage routes, such as the Puerco River, moisture retained in the soil between rains permitted farming to continue. The people gradually concentrated at a few sites near the more dependable water supplies. The many scattered small villages and summer farming sites were abandoned. Permanent villages developed and grew to large size.

Near the intersection of the park road and Puerco River is the ruin of a large masonry pueblo, Puerco Indian Ruin. It consisted of approximately 150 rooms arranged in a hollow square enclosing a large plaza containing several underground ceremonial chambers, or kivas. There were at least two rows of rooms all around the square, three rows in places, and part of the pueblo may have been two stories high. Rooms on the outside of the pueblo were primarily storage rooms while inside rows were mostly living quarters. There were no doors or windows in exterior walls, and entry was made via holes or hatchways in the log, brush, and mud roof. One could move from room to room within each house unit in the pueblo via very small doorways in the interior walls. It is estimated that the pueblo had a population of 200 to 250 persons at its peak.

The villagers farmed the natural terraces along the Puerco River flood plain, where their corn, beans, and squash might find adequate moisture in the river sand even though the river itself was often dry. The pueblo was abandoned about 1400, apparently because the area had become unlivable. There is no evidence that the pueblo residents were driven away by conflict with other Indians, no evidence of battles or epidemic disease.

The Puerco village had evolved because of the severe recurring droughts of the 1200's. The altered way of life, which must have been accompanied by many cultural changes, was an adaptation to a changing environment. It was successful adaptation, permitting the people to remain here 100 to 200 years longer than would otherwise have been possible. Weather patterns gradually changed after the droughts, however, and adaptation to the later environmental changes became necessary.

Following the droughts of the 1200's, rainfall increased greatly in the 1300's. Instead of reverting to the pre-1200 weather pattern, however, much of the annual precipitation was concentrated in the winter months. Rainfall was no longer distributed throughout the spring and summer; what rain came in summer was probably concentrated into short, violent thunderstorms. With the increasing winter rainfall and heavy summer storms, the Puerco River began to actively erode the terraces along its banks. Erosion of the terraces gradually eliminated Puerco farmlands, and summer weather patterns prevented farming elsewhere. The villagers depended upon their crops and the crops depended upon the floodplain terraces. Food production decreased. Unable to adapt to the change in environment that eliminated the crops, the Indians had the option of remaining and dying or moving in search of a more suitable area. The Puerco Village people in all likelihood collected most of their belongings and, if Hopi Indian tradition is correct, began a trek of 80 miles northwest to the Hopi pueblos which were built during the drought but which have survived to the present.

Throughout the park, other evidence of prehistoric Indian activity may be found. At an outcrop of coarse sandstone that was pulverized to mix with pottery clay, hammerstones still lie about as the women left them several hundred years ago. Any place in and near the park, spear and arrow points may be found. In the vicinity of ruins, pieces of broken pottery litter the ground, and rarely, an unbroken bowl may be found.

One of the most obvious indications of Indian activity is the thousands of petroglyphs pecked into the surface of sandstone blocks throughout the park. The sandstone in this area, when exposed to weathering over long periods, sometimes develops a very thin dark surface layer called desert varnish. The unweathered rock beneath the thin "varnish" is much lighter in color. By pecking away the dark sur-face with a sharp, hard rock (petrified wood, probably) the Indians created designs that showed very clearly when the lighter rock was exposed. Petroglyph designs include geometric patterns from simple to very complex, human and animal figures from tiny to almost life size, and various clan symbols. Others may be of ceremonial significance and many may simply be "doodling."

Many park visitors enjoy identifying the various items represented in the rock art, and some attempt to construct stories that the petroglyphs seem to tell. Try it, it may be more fun than you think, but do not place *too* much faith in the stories you build.

It is thus far not possible to measure the age of individual petroglyphs. The rate at which desert varnish develops depends upon so many variable factors that it is of no use in measuring time. A design or figure made at one time may be adjacent to one made 25, 50, or 100 years later and appear to be of similar age. Two petroglyphs of the same age may well have been made by different individuals representing different cultures. And one artist may, of course, have decided to "improve" the work of another.

One occasionally notices groups of petroglyphs on a smooth rock face 12-15 feet above ground level.

EXISTENCE IS NOT WON *without a struggle, and an inhospitable environment may make the conflict unending. In shifting soils and with infrequent rain, a marginal existence is a major success.*

With no hand holds or ledges, how did the artist execute his work so far up? He did it standing on the ground, probably, and erosion has since washed away the surface on which he stood, gradually lowering it to our level. If there is a "fresh" scar on the rock, one can sometimes find a sandstone slab that would fit into it. In such cases, the slab may have provided a ledge to support the artist 500 to 1000 years ago.

The world changes about us, but so slowly that we seldom notice. Or, if we notice, we (through our technology) gradually produce adaptations to the change. The Indians of the Southwest in the 1300's could not adapt to the water and farmland problems. We face a water problem today, but ours is a world-wide shortage of *good* water. We have allowed our technology to race ahead in the field of water pollution without requiring it to also perfect methods of water purification and reuse. The Indians here, when faced with a water shortage, could either die or move. Our present situation is somewhat different: We can't move.

DISCOVERY AND ESTABLISHMENT OF THE PARK

The occurrence of petrified wood in what is now Petrified Forest National Park was not reported until about the middle of the nineteenth century. Previously, some of the Spanish explorers had mentioned the painted desert, but apparently they did not see or recognize the petrified wood. It remained for U.S. Army Captain Lorenzo Sitgreaves, leading an 1851 exploration of New Mexico and Arizona, to be the first to describe the petrified wood, which was discovered on September 28, in an area several miles south of what is now the Park.

Knowledge of and interest in the "petrified forests" spread rapidly. U.S. Army General William T. Sherman, while on a tour of the west, suggested that two of the famous petrified logs be collected for the Smithsonian Institution in Washington, D.C. In the spring of 1879, a small detail was sent from Fort Wingate, New Mexico, to collect the required specimens.

After a dry and dusty trip, the detail arrived at Bear Spring near the head of Lithodendron Wash, where they set up camp. Also camped nearby were a number of Navajo Indians who ". . . thought it strange the 'Great Father in Washington' should want some of the bones of the 'Great Giant' their forefathers had killed years ago when taking possession of the country . . ." Two segments of a partly buried log which fit the requirements outlined by General Sherman were located about one and a quarter miles below Bear Springs. Both segments were loaded on wagons and hauled to Fort Wingate. One was shipped to Washington, D.C. and was subsequently put on display in the National Museum, where it remains today.

In 1883, the Atlantic and Pacific Railroad was completed through central Arizona, following the course of the Puerco River through what was to become the National Park. With completion of the railway travel to northern Arizona increased rapidly, and the "petrified forests" became the object of rapidly increasing visitation.

In 1890, the town of Adamana was established (about 15 miles north of what was then still called Chalcedony Park), providing a place where transcontinental trains could stop for water and coal and to permit passengers to dine. Adamana soon became the headquarters for tours of the petrified forests and a hotel was built to accommodate the visitors' needs. The Santa Fe Railway, successors to the Atlantic and Pacific, encouraged passengers to visit, and published brochures advertising the area.

As visitation increased, more and more of the petrified wood was carried off. Large logs were often dynamited by people searching for the crystals they sometimes contained. At Adamana, a mill was built for the purpose of crushing petrified wood into abrasives. This incident convinced Arizona territorial residents that the petrified forests would soon be a thing of the past unless permanent protection could be provided. Thus, in 1895, the Arizona territorial legislature petitioned the United States Congress to have the area occupied by Chalcedony Park set aside as a national park.

Lester Ward, a paleobotanist with U.S. Geological Survey, examined the area in 1899 and recommended that it be withdrawn from entry by homesteaders and established as a National Park. On June

PHOTOGRAPHS BY MIKE MCKELVEY

RESISTANT LAYERS *of sandstone or lava protect softer underlying rocks, causing mesas to develop. As the edge of the mesa slowly erodes, the exposed sediment melts quickly into the seemingly endless plain.* FRAGMENTS OF THE ANCIENT FOREST *(and occasional animal fossils) speckle the plain, seeming immune to the effects of erosion. But logs become chunks, then chips, and eventually are grains of quartz that follow the finer sediments toward the sea.*

23

8, 1906, the Congress passed the Antiquities Act. Six months later, on December 8, President Theodore Roosevelt utilized the provisions of that act to set aside the Nation's second National Monument, Petrified Forest National Monument. In several steps over many years, the Monument was enlarged to its present size; the area was designated as a National Park in 1962.

The wisdom of governmental control of the area is indisputable. Unprotected petrified wood deposits in the region have been greatly depleted over the ensuing years for commercial purposes and by souvenir hunters. Because of farsighted conservationists of the 1890's and early 1900's, at least some of the world's greatest deposits of petrified wood have been preserved for the enjoyment of our generation and for the future. The battle to preserve it for the future

is continued today by the National Park Service. Petrified wood is no longer hauled out by the trainload, and the thoughtless and selfish are no longer permitted to blast open logs in the hopes there might be valuable crystals in them. Today no one proposes that the wood be converted to abrasives, but over 25 *thousand* pounds of wood leaves the Park each year.

Certain fellow citizens, most of them basically honest people who wouldn't think of stealing a candy bar from the grocery store or a newspaper from an unattended stand, are blithely stealing their children's heritage. There seems to be a lot of petrified wood in the park (and there is), but there was once much more. As it is always the prettiest pieces that they sneak away with, the beauty of the park is steadily diminished.

IN THE GRAVEYARD *of the Navajos'* *legendary giants, their ancient* *"bones" mellow in the summer* *sun. New life is seen where* *the Puerco River meanders* *through a border of young trees* *and green slopes in another part* *of the park. But where the* *great forest was, the timeless* *winds still blow across the* *flatland grasses and etch* *the remaining bluffs.*

NATIONAL PARK SERVICE

MIKE MCKELVEY

Petty shoplifting is bad enough, but it is at least only the theft of replaceable manufactured items from an individual. Petrified wood thieves, however, are stealing an irreplaceable monument to 200 million years of development and are stealing it from all of us *and from future generations.*

Admire the wood; examine it. Pick up pieces of it and look at them closely. Enjoy the colors and pattern that make the piece you hold unique. Consider the thousands of other park visitors who may have the same pleasant experience with that same piece of petrified wood *if you leave it·for those others to enjoy.*

SUGGESTED READING

MERA, H. P., "Observations on the Archeology of the Petrified Forest National Monument", *Laboratory of Anthropology,* Technical Series, Bulletin No. 7, Santa Fe. 1934.

SCHROEDER, A. H., "Puerco Ruin Excavations, Petrified Forest National Monument, Arizona," *Plateau,* V. 33, No. 4, Flagstaff, Arizona.

WENDORF, FRED, with sections by KENT, K. P., MORRIS, EARL H., and SHEPARD, A. O., *Archeological Studies in the Petrified Forest National Monument,* Museum of Northern Arizona Bulletin 27, Flagstaff, Arizona. 1953.

WORMINGTON, H. M., *Prehistoric Indians of the Southwest,* Denver Museum of Natural History, Denver, Colorado. 1951.

MOLLHAUSEN, BALDWIN, *Diary of a Journey from the Mississippi to the Coasts of the Pacific with a United States Government Expedition,* London, 2 Vols. 1858.

SITGREAVES, LORENZO, *Report of an Expedition Down the Zuni and Colorado Rivers,* U.S. Govt. Printing Office. 1854.

WHIPPLE, AMIEL WEEKS and Other, *Report of Explorations for a Railway Route . . . from the Mississippi River to the Pacific Ocean,* U.S. Govt. Printing Office, Washington, D.C. 1856. An abridged edition of the report has been published as "A Pathfinder in the Southwest" by the University of Oklahoma Press. 1941.

Petrified Forest Today

Visitors to northeastern Arizona are often surprised by the predominantly grass and brush vegetation. "But where are the cactus?" is not an uncommon question from newcomers to Arizona. Cactus plants do occur here, but the great saguaro and organ pipe cacti, the Joshua tree and other spectacular succullents are limited to the true deserts south and west of Petrified Forest.

Residents of Arizona's northeastern plateau (a part of the much larger Colorado Plateau) often speak of their surroundings as "desert", but technically the vegetation type here is short grass plains or desert shrub. The term "desert grassland" is often used. Whatever one calls it, the area contains a complex and fascinating combination of plants and animals. To many people, terms such as "barren", "desolate" and even "dull" seem an accurate description. To those who know it, or those who will look at it with a questing eye, this land is filled with life, color, and form.

Climate sets the theme here, as it does everywhere. Wind and water carve the landscape, creating some soils and removing others, thus controlling the plants that follow. Moisture and sunlight, with temperature and wind, impose further limits on the vegetation. Vegetation and weather greatly influence the selection of wildlife that can survive here. Some forms of wildlife control others or certain plants. This is not a straight chain of single links but a mesh, a web of life, *supported* by air, light, land, and water, but *influenced* by every strand of the web.

A major strand in the web of life here, as everywhere, is the dominant creature—you. Man is as much a part of the web as are the grass and antelope, but man's influence on the other strands is infinitely greater. Each part of the web supports the others above the abyss of extinction. Small parts of the web, individual strands, may fall off or be removed without danger to the whole, but if enough threads are destroyed the remaining parts will be too weak to support the rest.

Indians at Petrified Forest led a life more closely integrated with the other strands in the web of which he was a part than does modern man. He was without doubt the dominant life form, but his effect on the other parts was less and their influence on him was greater than in our case. Indians were a part of their ecology and we cannot escape being a part of ours. Our success in changing (some say destroying) our environment may provide the ultimate answer to the population explosion problem.

Climate sets the theme, and here the climate is one of extremes and occasional violence. The annual precipitation averages only about nine inches (most major U.S. cities get 25-50 inches) and half of it comes in short violent thunderstorms in July, August, and September. Before the summer rainy season May, June, and sometimes early July are typically very dry. About half of the year's precipitation is received in showers and snow scattered throughout the rest of the year.

Brief snowstorms are not uncommon in winter, but the snow is rarely deep and seldom remains very long. Sub-zero temperatures are not uncommon on winter nights and even in bright sunshine subfreezing temperatures can persist all day. Even in mid-winter, however, moderate afternoon temperatures are not unusual.

Typically, in summer, the temperature rises to 100° or very slightly higher on just a few days in July and averages in the low 90's for much of the summer. In common with most desert and grassland areas, night temperatures are very much lower than in daytime.

High winds may occur at any time and usually cause dust and sand storms along dry stream beds and denuded land. Where grass and brush are not excluded by natural causes or have not been destroyed by man's influence, blowing sand and dust are seldom a problem.

Weather, with other influences, selects the vegetation and wildlife that may live on the land. Plants must evolve very efficient methods of collecting or

ALTHOUGH NORTHERN ARIZONA *does not share in the magnificent flower displays of the true desert, spring and summer are bright with varied color.* THE PINCUSHION, *other cacti, and dozens of other flowering plants occur throughout most of the park south of the Painted Desert, which supports little vegetation of any kind.* MARIPOSA LILIES *bloom in May if there has been moisture enough in the preceding few months.*

storing water to survive in an area of limited rainfall. They must compete with their neighbors for what moisture becomes available. Perennial plants must collect some water during even the driest part of the year, while annuals must pass the dry seasons in a dormant form, such as a seed.

Cacti and others may utilize a widespread shallow root system to absorb great quantities of water near the surface during rains and then store it in their fleshy stems. Did you ever notice that a cactus has no leaves? It is all stem. Water is stored in the stems and evaporation loss is limited by a waxy coating outside the stem. Some animals that would eat the cactus for food or for the stored moisture are deterred by the sharp spines (which are really modified leaves).

Yucca plants, even more than cacti, are typical of the entire Southwest. Two species of yucca are found at Petrified Forest and their relatives are found throughout the arid Southwest. Yuccas were and still are much used by Indians, for the plants provide several products which the Indians adapted to their use. The long, thin, needle sharp leaves provide fibers for weaving and the plant root is used in preparing a soap. The fat seed pods serve as food.

Yuccas are partners in a remarkable relationship with the pronuba moth. The relationship is an example of symbiosis, the situation where two organisms develop adaptations to each other that make them mutually dependent.

Pronuba moths lay their eggs only in the base of the yucca blossom; the pronubas do not exist where there are no yuccas. Yucca plants, however, are fertilized only by the pronuba moths and cannot reproduce unless the moths are present. The female moth injects several eggs into the base of a blossom, where the larvae will have access to developing seeds. The moth, after laying several eggs, climbs to the (male) anther of the flower, collects the sticky pollen, and rolls it into a ball. She carries the ball of pollen to the flower's pistil (female) and pushes the pollen into the opening at the top of the pistil. The moth thus fertilizes the blossom, assuring that seeds are produced and that the moth larvae will have a food supply. The larvae eat some of the developing seeds, mature, and drop out of the seed capsule. The uneaten seeds continue to grow, ripen, and also drop to the ground.

No other insects pollinate yucca blossoms, nor is the sticky pollen carried by the wind. Pronubas do not lay their eggs in other flowers. Each organism requires and supports the other. If the unwise use of insecticides or other pollutants were to eliminate pronuba moths, yuccas would eventually disappear.

Have you ever wondered how many values we may unintentionally lose if we do not soon learn to control pollution?

Other plants have also evolved a waxy "water-proofing" to reduce moisture loss and a few even share the cactuses leafless habit. Mormon tea, a common shrub, consists of green, jointed twigs with tiny scale like leaves. Annual plants that pass the winter as seeds and many grasses that overwinter in a dormant condition avoid the water shortage in dry summers by simply not growing. The seeds and dormant plants remain in that condition until the next year brings rain.

During your trip through Petrified Forest, take the time to get out of your car and look at the vegetation. Look for the adaptations discussed above. Note, too, that what may first appear to be an unbroken mat of vegetation is, in fact, a large number of individual plants separated from their neighbors by bare ground. Even the grasses do not usually carpet an area like a lawn or eastern grassland. The regular spacing of plants may result from competition for moisture or from a "defensive" adaptation that prohibits the growth of other plants.

If water competition causes the spacing, it simply means that under the conditions at that place there is only enough water to support the plants which you see. New plants cannot establish themselves in the open ground between plants because the roots of older plants absorb all the water. New plants may start to grow, but quickly die from lack of moisture. Should an older plant die or be removed, a replacement will shortly spring up at the same place.

Some plants have evolved a more sophisticated adaptation that carries them a step further. Chemical compounds produced by their roots or released by their decaying leaves prevent other plants from growing nearby. The other plants are prevented from growing nearby either by an inhibitor which slows the root growth of a competitor or by a toxin that kills the competitor outright.

Plants in any area must adapt to survive, and must do so at that point where they grow. Animals must also adapt to their environment, but can get up and move away from a local inhospitable influence. They rarely move far, however, and either adapt to their surroundings or cease to exist. The environment changes, usually very slowly, and all inhabitants must develop new adaptations over many generations or they are excluded. If the environment is changed rapidly, the survival of any species becomes highly unlikely. The nature of *our* environ-

SEED CAPSULES *tell of the success of a relationship between fineleaf yucca plants and the pronuba moth. Yuccas will not produce seeds unless pronubas fertilize the flowers, and the moth cannot reproduce unless the yucca produces seeds. So the moth places pollen on the plant's stigma, insuring a seed crop, and lays her eggs in the capsule where her offspring will eat some of the seeds. Not all the seeds are eaten, and both plant and insect benefit from the exchange.*

MIKE MCKELVEY

29

ment is changing rapidly today, and our survival is open to question.

Migration is one adaptation to the changing seasons that does involve long distance travel. Most summer resident birds at Petrified Forest are dependent upon a diet of live insects. Such birds depart for southern points about the time that the insect supply declines in autumn. Other birds adapt to the changing seasons by changing from a summer diet of insects to one of seeds in winter.

Unable to migrate, many small mammals have evolved adaptations such as food storage or hibernation. Many rodents store fruit, seeds, or dried vegetation in underground chambers. They then sleep most of the winter (without going into true hibernation), awaking occasionally to feed. Mammals that hibernate live on food stored as fat within their bodies. In hibernation, bodily processes (heartbeat, breathing, etc.) slow down to a very low level, more like "suspended animation" than sleep.

Reptiles and amphibians at Petrified Forest share the hibernation habit. The common gopher snake, which is large and handsomely patterned, the brightly colored king snake, and the rarely seen praire rattlesnake disappear in fall and are not seen again until spring. Many species of lizards are present throughout the park, and visitors are likely to see them at any of the points of interest. The brilliantly colored collared lizard and the numerous

other species of lizards disappear from the scene each winter. The spadefoot toad and tiger salamander also hibernate.

Predators, both birds and mammals, undergo little change in what they eat, but may experience difficulty in finding enough to eat in winter. Bobcats, coyotes, and foxes range farther and spend more hours seeking jackrabbits, cottontails, birds, and other prey in winter.

As there are no lakes or permanent streams in the park, water supply is a problem for animals as much as for plants. The adaptations of wildlife to the arid environment are many and varied. Some of the

NATIONAL PARK SERVICE

larger mammals such as the pronghorn "antelope" and wide ranging birds such as golden eagles and ravens may periodically visit water holes outside the park. During the summer rainy season there is usually an ample water supply. For most of the year, however, and in the occasional summer of drought, water supplies may be critical. The kangaroo rat has evolved a very sophisticated adaptation to the arid lands; it *manufactures* water. The unique ability to chemically manufacture water while living on a totally dry diet, and an extremely efficient urinary system that conserves water in the body make the kangaroo rat quite independent of liquid water supplies.

Dew, frost, and snow provide an irregular supply of moisture that may be adequate for some animals. Others may gain enough moisture from plants which they eat. In dry periods, some may force their way past cactus spines to eat the spongy wet tissue of the plant. Water is usually close to the surface in dry stream beds, and bobcats or coyotes may dig holes to get water.

Environmental adaptations may seem endlessly varied. Each is the product of eons of change in response to the sum of all of the effects of the environment. Changes in the environment usually take place gradually over very long periods. Successive generations of plants and animals adjust to minor changes in their life times. If environmental changes are rapid, there is no time to adapt. Some species for a time may persist in the changing world, leading a progressively poorer existence. When environmental changes exceed a species' limit of toleration, however, that species dies.

The desert grassland web of life, supported like other webs by soil, water, air and light, is a resilient network which evolved over eons of time. Early man lived a life integrated into that web. More recently, we have imposed new tensions and pressures. The introduction of the "new wildlife," the cattle, sheep, goats, horses, and others, has wrenched entire sections of the web into a new shape that cannot long endure. The over-utilization of some food plants by stock has opened the way for increases in other plants. Vegetation changes force immediate and large scale changes in wildlife; some species disappear, others increase explosively. Each change triggers others and as the ecology "runs wild," the web of life trembles.

In some places overuse of the land has removed the protecting vegetation and soil erosion has increased manifold. Water runs off the soil rapidly where much of it once was absorbed and with it go tons of soil. Downstream, the silt mixes with sewage and industrial pollutants and the water is unfit. Most windblown soil settles back to earth, but a small amount is carried aloft where it absorbs a tiny but significant amount of sunlight; there it also mixes with pollutants that combine chemically with the oxygen that is critical to all animal life.

There are those who say that "now" is too late; respected scientists who say that our technology has wrought changes in our environment that are beyond the point of no return. They claim that continued absorption of sunlight by airborne particles, loss of available oxygen through its chemical combination with other pollutants, the loss of usable water and other factors have already initiated a course of events that can only end in collapse of our environment and the end of our civilization.

Other, equally reputable, scientists argue that the process of self-destruction has not yet reached an irreversible point. They agree that we are poised on the verge of oblivion, but insist that there is yet time to move back from the edge. There is little argument that a point of no return *exists*, the only point of discussion is whether it has been passed or not. There is no doubt that today we possess the technology to reverse the trend, *if* we have the time.

The National Park Service has accepted the *belief* that some time remains and the *hope* that it will be enough. Joining with other Federal and local governmental agencies, private groups and educational

31

A MASSIVE *petrified tree behind the Rainbow Forest Museum is the largest log that most visitors see. It has somehow gained the unlikely name of "Old Faithful," and is examined and remembered by thousands of visitors.*

DAVID MUENCH

institutions, the National Park Service in 1968 embarked upon a massive education and information program. The program was not instituted to present arguments for more parks. Although it follows that tomorrow's people, *if there are any*, will require recreation lands of many kinds, the environmental conservation program transcends that need. The several facets of the program are intended to acquaint people with the threat of oblivion and to urge upon us the industrial, political, financial and personal changes that must be made quickly.

You *are* involved. Whether you are involved as an active participant or as one who stands aside and thereby contributes to the dissolution of civilization is a decision you must make. And you have to make that decision now . . .

SUGGESTED READING

DEPARTMENT OF INTERIOR, *Man . . . An Endangered Species?* Conservation Yearbook No. 4, U.S. Govt. Printing Office. 1968.

LEOPOLD, ALDO, *A Sand County Almanac*, Oxford University Press. 1966.

OSBORN, FAIRFIELD, *Our Plundered Planet*, Little, Brown & Co. 1948.

STORER, JOHN H., *The Web of Life*, Devin Publishing Co. (hardbound) or New American Library (paperback).

UDALL, STEWART L., *The Quiet Crisis*, Holt, Rinehart & Winston, Inc., New York, N.Y. 10017. 1963.

Inside back cover: Petrified logs in the Blue Mesa area, by Josef Muench.

Back cover: Blue Mesa — a vast expanse of colorful shale beds, by Wayne Davis.